This book belongs to

The King's Horse

A Purim Story

By Leah Sokol

Illustrated by
Joni Aliza Boroda

ISBN-13: 978-1722027933
ISBN-10: 1722027932
Copyright © 2019 Leah Sokol

Published in conjunction with Torah Umesorah
The National Society for Hebrew Day Schools

Dedications

To Zisha
(Chaim Alexander Ziskind Rosenberg)
who inspired me to write picture books.

Leah Sokol

To my sister Beth,
and our childhood love of horses.
And to my parents,
who worked long hours and extra jobs
so that we could ride.

Joni Aliza Boroda

1

I am the king's horse. It is not an easy job. But it is a very important job.

I live in the biggest stall in the Persian royal stables. Sometimes, I am lonely. King Achashverosh never comes to visit me. He is a busy man, always planning parties, wars, and then more parties. So he lets the stable boys take care of me.

But the stable boys are always in a rush. They are rough and don't talk to me. And they never give me carrots.

The other horses are my friends. We like to talk about the people in the palace. King Achashverosh and Queen Vashti throw such crazy parties! And then there's Haman, the king's sly adviser. His last brilliant idea was to command that everyone in the kingdom bow to him!

When humans get boring—and they do—we horses like to race. I always win the races.

King Achashverosh chose me to be his horse for two reasons. First, because I am so handsome. And second, because I run so fast.

I am proud to be the king's horse.

Except when the king decides to ride me.

Getting ready takes an hour. Fancy blankets are arranged on my back. Jewels are attached to my saddle. They even braid my hair. A braided tail is useless for swatting flies.

And *then*, four hundred pounds are dumped on my back.

Let me tell you something else. King Achashverosh
is not a great rider. He's always digging his heels into
my belly. He has no balance at all. He feels like a sack
of bricks.

It is a very hard job. But it is my job. I am the most
famous horse in the land.

Bow to Haman? *Phht*. If people were smart, they
would bow to me.

All the other horses were very busy. Queen Vashti was dead, and the king was having a beauty contest. The winner would become the new queen. Every day, my friends carried new girls into the castle. None of the horses had time to talk or race.

And those girls! They were all loaded down with gowns and jewelry. One girl, Esther, cried all over her horse! I guess not everyone wants to be queen.

I didn't have to help. I am the king's horse. That means only the king may ride me.

But I felt sorry for my friends.

It was still better than having Queen Vashti around. For her last party, she dyed all our tails purple! Even with all the extra work, none of us horses were sorry she was gone.

And things got much better once Esther became queen.

"No more pulling wagons of clothes to the palace!" my friend Dancer said happily. "The new queen doesn't care what she wears."

"But there will be less hunting," grumbled another horse. "The new queen doesn't eat meat. Did you ever hear of anything so ridiculous?"

"Why won't she eat meat?" Cassia popped her nose out of her oats. Only talk about food can get Cassia's attention.

"Nobody knows," Dancer said. "Nobody knows anything about her. She won't even tell the king where she's from!"

"Kind of strange, if you ask me," Cassia said, and went back to crunching her oats.

3

Finally, things went back to normal. Until one day, Mordechai the Jew showed up in the courtyard. He looked sad. He was wearing a black bag over his body. And he had ashes sprinkled on his head.

Let me tell you something about ashes. They make horses sneeze.

Mordechai was always different. He didn't care about parties or wine! That's all the other humans care about. He wouldn't bow down to Haman, either. That made Haman angry.

And every morning, Mordechai walked around and around the palace. He asked every person he met, "Is Queen Esther all right? Is she safe? Is she happy?"

It made me wonder if Esther was Jewish, too. She even smells a little bit like Mordechai. Maybe they're related. If Esther is Jewish, that explains why she won't eat meat. Jews have rules about what they're allowed to eat.

It also explains why she won't tell the king who she is. Everyone knows Haman hates the Jews. Maybe she's afraid of him.

Sometimes, Mordechai brought apples and carrots for the horses. So I thought he was all right. Until he started walking around with ashes on his head.

Humans. There's no point in trying to figure them out.

Not long after that, I woke up to silence. The stable was completely empty.

There were no horses or humans in sight. I neighed three times. Finally, a stable boy hurried in.

"Sorry!" the stable boy said. "It's been so busy! I forgot all about you."

About me! Me, the king's horse! I flattened my ears and glared at him.

The stable boy began brushing out my mane. Just then, Dancer was led into the stable. He was covered with sweat and breathing hard.

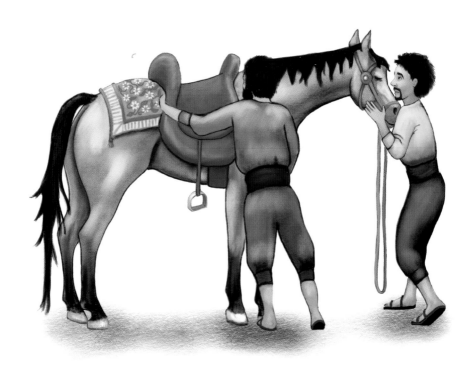

"Change his saddle quickly," Dancer's stable boy said. "We need to send him out again right away. We have to get the king's message out. It must reach every city in the kingdom!"

"But there aren't enough horses!" my stable boy said.

Dancer's stable boy sighed. "We have no choice. Haman wants the messages sent immediately."

"Typical royalty," my stable boy grumbled. "They decide to kill all the Jews in the kingdom. But who has to do all the work? We do!"

"Actually," Dancer snorted, "I think it's me doing the work."

I nickered in sympathy. But deep down, I was just glad it wasn't me. If I was used as a common messenger horse, the king would never ride me again.

So I remained right where I was.

At least now I knew why Mordechai had ashes on his head. He was showing how sad he was about the decree.

For the next few weeks, the stable was mostly empty. I was lonelier than ever. But then my friends came back. Everything went back to normal. For a little while.

I was in the middle of my favorite dream. I was running through a field covered with carrots. Oats rained down on me from the sky. Suddenly, a shout woke me up.

I blinked, then closed my eyes. I tried to go back to sleep. But the shout came again. "Who enters the courtyard?"

"It is I, Haman!" came the answer. "I must speak to the king about punishing Mordechai!"

I opened my eyes and flicked my tail. Across from me, Dancer was also awake. He snorted unhappily. A steady chomp-chomp came from the stall in the corner. Cassia was awake, too.

"You may see the king," the guard announced. The gates to the castle clanged shut.

"Finally," Dancer grumbled. He closed his eyes and dropped his head. Within seconds, he was snoring.

I wasn't so lucky. I tried everything to get back to sleep. I counted hoof prints. I paced in my stall. I closed my eyes and listened to Dancer's snoring. Nothing worked.

I had a bad feeling. I didn't know what exactly Haman wanted, but something told me I wouldn't like it.

I was right.

6

Early the next morning, a stable boy woke me up. I had just fallen asleep. But I picked my knees up as I trotted into the courtyard.

I am, after all, the king's horse. I must look noble and dignified. Even when all I want to do is sleep.

A man walked toward me. But it wasn't the king.

It was Mordechai.

Mordechai was dressed in the king's clothes (which were way too big on him). He was wearing the king's crown (which was so bright it made me blink).

And behind Mordechai stood Haman. Haman was wearing his usual clothes. He did not look happy.

Next thing I knew, Mordechai was boosted onto my back.

I squealed in outrage. Haman hit my hindquarters with a whip. I considered kicking him.

"By the king's command," Haman grumbled, "Mordechai will ride through the city on the king's horse. I will lead him."

The stable boys looked at each other. They were trying not to laugh.

"Mordechai saved the king's life a few years ago," one whispered to the other. "He's being rewarded."

"And it was Haman's idea!" the second stable boy snickered. "The king asked him about ways to honor people. Haman thought the king was going to honor him!"

Haman grabbed my bridle and pulled it. I decided to make the best of a bad situation. I held my head high. I stepped proudly across the cobblestones. I pretended it was the king on my back.

But Mordechai didn't feel like the king. He was a lot lighter. He didn't dig his heels into my sides. He didn't use his whip on me. I realized that I was enjoying myself.

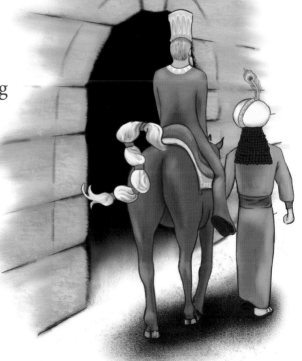

Until I heard a crinkling sound and jerked my head up. A stream of garbage was pouring down from above. I stopped short.

And the garbage landed all over Haman instead of on me.

Haman screamed and let go of the reins. He tried to cover his head. But it was too late. Garbage poured over his face. It dripped down his hair. It trickled into his clothes.

Some horses would have run from that stink. But I am the king's horse. I stood perfectly still. Finally, Haman grabbed the reins again.

(I might have laughed, a tiny bit. But to Haman it just sounded like a snort.)

Mordechai stroked my neck. He whispered, "Good horse. Thank you."

After that, Haman jerked my reins harder than ever. The smell of garbage was right in my nose. Even so, it was the most fun I'd had in years.

7

The next day, Mordechai came to my stall. He gave me a carrot.

"Thank you again," he said. "Haman's daughter threw that garbage. She was aiming at me. If not for you, I would have been covered with filth."

I chomped the carrot happily. But Mordechai wasn't happy. I could see the sadness in his face.

Mordechai was a Jew. Soon he, too, would be killed. Along with all the other Jews.

The carrot suddenly didn't taste as good. I nudged Mordechai's shoulder with my muzzle.

"Don't worry," Mordechai said. It was like he understood what I was thinking. "Haman convinced King Achashverosh that the Jews should be killed. But we have a secret weapon in the palace—the queen herself. I was so sad when Esther was chosen to be queen. But now I see that it was part of the Creator's plan. He will save us."

Straw rustled. A servant stepped into the stable.

Mordechai turned.

"A message from Queen Esther," the servant said. "She has invited the king and Haman to another party tomorrow. There, she will beg the king to spare her people. All Jews should continue praying for her."

Mordechai nodded. "We will."

That afternoon, the king rode me around the city. I walked extra smoothly, so he would be comfortable. I wanted him in a good mood for Queen Esther's party.

8

That evening, my dinner was interrupted by Haman's screams. I looked out of my stall. Two servants were dragging Haman across the courtyard.

King Achashverosh followed them. He yelled, "How dare you attack the queen! Hang him at once!"

Even Cassia stopped eating long enough to watch.

I flicked my ears. I guess the party went well for Queen Esther. And I guess it didn't go so well for Haman.

Too bad nobody knows that it was all thanks to me.

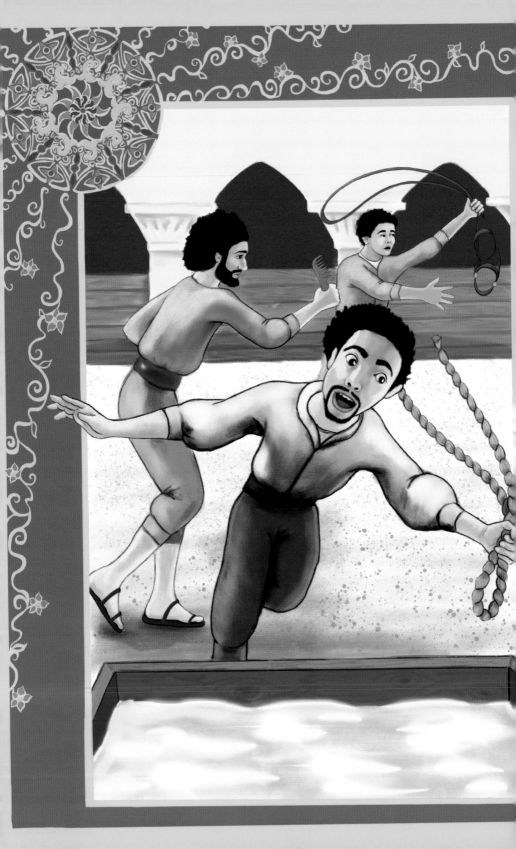

9

A few months later, I woke up to find the stable boys in a frenzy. They rushed in. They rushed out. They grabbed saddles. They threw bridles to each other. One stable boy tripped over a grooming brush. He fell face-first into the water trough.

"We need the fastest horses!" my stable boy shouted. "The king has decreed that the Jews may defend themselves. The messages must be sent to the whole kingdom. They must reach every city before the 13th day of the month of Adar. We don't have much time!"

"But we don't have enough horses," another stable boy said. "And no horse can get to the farthest city that fast."

One by one, all my friends galloped out of the stable. Each carried the message that Esther had begged for. Each would help save the Jews.

But not me. Because I was the king's horse.

I wanted to help. But how could I be ridden by a common messenger? It would mean I couldn't be the king's horse ever again.

I pawed at the straw. Then I made up my mind. I kicked down the door of my stall. I raced into the courtyard.

In the confusion, no one recognized me. One of the newer stable boys saddled me up. Next thing I knew, a messenger was on my back.

I galloped as fast as I could. We reached the farthest city just in time. The king's message was delivered.

And all the Jews in the kingdom were saved.

10

Many days later, I trotted back into the city. I was exhausted. I made my way through the Jewish quarter. People were celebrating. Finally, I trudged into the castle courtyard.

I headed for my usual stall. The stable master grabbed my reins. He pulled me back.

"It's all right," one stable boy said. "I recognize this one. He is the king's horse."

"He can't be," the stable master said. "He's been ridden by a common messenger. Put him in a regular stall. He's not the king's horse anymore."

When I woke up the next morning, I smelled carrots.
Two carrots. No—three. Mordechai was holding them. He was standing in my stall. His face wasn't sad any more.

He gave me a carrot. Then he said, "The king told me that you are not his horse anymore."

My neck drooped.

"I am the king's new adviser," Mordechai said. "I asked him for a gift."

I stopped chewing the carrot.

"I asked him for you," Mordechai said. "You are my horse now. Let's take a ride through the city. We can watch the celebrations."

I arched my neck. For the first time, I couldn't wait to be ridden.

But first, I finished the rest of the carrots.

AFTERWORD

This is a horse's eye view of the story of Purim, recounted in Megillat Esther (the Scroll of Esther). Megillat Esther tells how, in the times of the Persian Empire, the king's adviser Haman convinced the king to issue a decree. The decree stated that on the 13th day of the Jewish month of Adar, the citizens of the Persian Empire would be permitted to rise up against the Jews who lived among them. They could kill them and take their property.

What Haman did not know was that the king's new queen, Esther, was secretly Jewish. He also did not know that Esther's uncle, Mordechai, had saved the king's life a few years before. Together, Mordechai and Esther arranged for the downfall of Haman. They then convinced the king to issue a new decree: that on the 13th day of Adar, the Jews would be allowed to defend themselves.

Everything was turned on its head. Haman was killed and Mordechai became the king's new adviser. The day after the battle, the 14th of Adar, became the holiday of Purim.

Even though it is a seemingly simple story, Megillat Esther contains many hints to all the political scheming going on behind the scenes. Many of these are explored through ancient commentaries called midrashim. One midrash tells how Haman's daughter, assuming it was Mordechai leading the horse, dumped garbage all over him—except "him" turned out to be Haman.

While some of the details in this book are taken from midrashim, most of them come straight from the author's imagination.

Horses have extremely keen hearing. Their ears can swivel all around, which helps them know exactly where any sound is coming from. Therefore, Achasheverosh's horse might have heard the garbage coming before any human did.

Horses only sleep two or three hours a day, and they usually sleep standing up. But that doesn't mean they like it when their sleep is interrupted!

And horses really, really like carrots.